Grammar minutes

100 minutes to practise and reinforce essential skills

Carmen S Jones

6327

Grammar minutes *Book 1*

Published by Prim-Ed Publishing® 2011 under licence to
Creative Teaching Press.
Copyright© 2009 Creative Teaching Press.
This version copyright©Prim-Ed Publishing® 2011

ISBN 978-1-84654-294-7
PR–6327

Titles available in this series:
Grammar minutes Book 1
Grammar minutes Book 2
Grammar minutes Book 3
Grammar minutes Book 4
Grammar minutes Book 5
Grammar minutes Book 6

Internet websites
In some cases, websites or specific URLs may be recommended. While these are checked and rechecked at the time of publication, the publisher has no control over any subsequent changes which may be made to webpages. It is *strongly* recommended that the class teacher checks *all* URLs before allowing pupils to access them.

View all pages online

Website: www.prim-ed.com

GRAMMAR MINUTES – BOOK 1

Foreword

Grammar minutes is a six-book series for primary school pupils that provides a structured daily programme of easy-to-follow activities in grammar. The main objective is grammar proficiency, attained by teaching pupils to apply grammar skills to answer questions effortlessly and rapidly. The questions in this book provide pupils with practice in the following key areas of grammar instruction:

- *sentences*
- *nouns*
- *pronouns*
- *capital letters*
- *verbs*
- *adjectives*
- *contractions*
- *compound words*
- *synonyms*
- *antonyms*
- *articles.*

Grammar minutes – Book 1 features 100 'minutes', each with 10 classroom-tested problems. Use this comprehensive resource to improve your pupils' overall grammar proficiency, which will promote greater self-confidence in their grammar skills as well as provide the everyday practice necessary to succeed in testing situations. Designed to be implemented in numerical order from 1 to 100, the activities in *Grammar minutes* are developmental through each book and across the series.

Comprehensive teachers notes, record-keeping charts, a scope-and-sequence table (showing when each new concept and skill is introduced), and photocopiable pupil reference materials are also included.

How many minutes does it take to complete a 'grammar minute'?

Pupils will enjoy challenging themselves as they apply their grammar knowledge and understanding to complete a 'grammar minute' in the fastest possible time.

Titles available in this series:

- *Grammar minutes – Book 1*
- *Grammar minutes – Book 2*
- *Grammar minutes – Book 3*
- *Grammar minutes – Book 4*
- *Grammar minutes – Book 5*
- *Grammar minutes – Book 6*

Contents

Teachers notes .... iv – viii

    How to use this book .... iv – v

    Minute records – Teacher record table vi

    Minute journal – Pupil record sheet vii

    Scope-and-sequence table viii

Grammar minutes 1–100 1–100

Answers 101–105

Teachers notes

How to use this book

Grammar minutes can be used in a variety of ways, such as:

- **a speed test**. As the teacher starts a stopwatch, pupils begin the 'minute'. As each pupil finishes, he/she raises a hand and the teacher calls out the time. The pupil records this time on the appropriate place on the sheet. Alternatively, a particular time can be allocated for the whole class to complete the 'minute' in. Pupils record their scores and time on their 'minute journal' (see page vii).

- **a whole-class activity**. Work through the 'minute' together as a teaching or reviewing activity.

- **a warm-up activity**. Use a 'minute' a day as a 'starter' or warm-up activity before the main part of the lesson begins.

- **a homework activity**. If given as a homework activity, it would be most beneficial for the pupils if the 'minute' is corrected and reviewed at the start of the following lesson.

Grammar minutes strategies

Encourage pupils to apply the following strategies to help improve their scores and decrease the time taken to complete the 10 questions.

- To use strategies whenever possible.
- To move quickly down the page, answering the problems they know first.
- To come back to problems they are unsure of, after they have completed all other problems.
- To make educated guesses when they encounter problems they are not familiar with.

A *Grammar minute* pupil activity page.

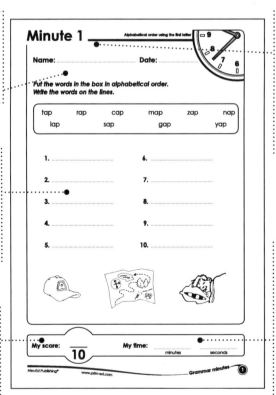

Name and date
Pupils write their name and the date in the spaces provided.

Questions
There are 10 problems, providing practice in every key area of grammar proficiency.

Score
Pupils record their score out of 10 in the space provided.

'Grammar minute' number
Grammar minutes are designed to be completed in numerical order.

Time
Pupils record the time taken to complete the 'minute' at the bottom of the sheet. (This is optional.)

Teachers notes

Marking

Answers are provided for all activities. How these activities are marked will vary according to the teacher's organisational policy. Methods could include whole-class checking, partner checking, individual pupil checking or collection by the teacher.

Diagnosis of problem areas

Grammar minutes provides the teacher with immediate feedback of whole-class and individual pupil understanding. This information is useful for future programming and planning of further opportunities to practise and review the skills and concepts which need addressing.

Make use of the structured nature of the questions to diagnose problem areas; rather than asking who got 10 out of 10, ask the pupils who got Question 1 correct to raise their hands, Question 2, Question 3 etc. In this way, you will be able to quickly determine which concepts are causing problems for the majority of the pupils. Once the routine of *Grammar minutes* is established, the teacher will have time to work with individuals or small groups to assist them with any areas causing problems.

Meeting the needs of individuals

The structure of *Grammar minutes* allows some latitude in the way the books are used; for example, it may be impractical (as well as demoralising for some) for all pupils to be using the same book. It can also be difficult for teachers to manage the range of abilities found in any one classroom, so while pupils may be working at different levels from different books, the familiar structure makes it easier to cope with individual differences. An outline of the suggested age range levels each book is suited to is given on page iii.

Additional resources:

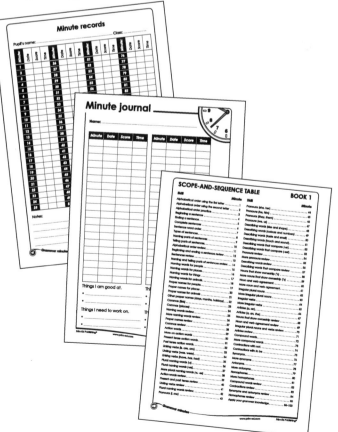

- **Minute records**

    Teachers can record pupil scores and times on the **Minute records** table located on page vi.

- **Scope and sequence**

    The **Scope-and-sequence table** gives the 'minute' in which each new skill and concept appears for the first time.

- **Minute journal**

    Once a 'minute' is completed, pupils record their score and time on their **Minute journal**, located on page vii.

- **Answers to all questions are found on pages 101 to 105.**

Minute records

Pupil's name: .... Class: ....

Minute:	Date	Score	Time	Minute:	Date	Score	Time	Minute:	Date	Score	Time	Minute:	Date	Score	Time
1				26				51				76			
2				27				52				77			
3				28				53				78			
4				29				54				79			
5				30				55				80			
6				31				56				81			
7				32				57				82			
8				33				58				83			
9				34				59				84			
10				35				60				85			
11				36				61				86			
12				37				62				87			
13				38				63				88			
14				39				64				89			
15				40				65				90			
16				41				66				91			
17				42				67				92			
18				43				68				93			
19				44				69				94			
20				45				70				95			
21				46				71				96			
22				47				72				97			
23				48				73				98			
24				49				74				99			
25				50				75				100			

Notes:

....

....

....

....

Minute journal

Name: ....

Minute	Date	Score	Time

Minute	Date	Score	Time

Things I am good at.

• ....

• ....

Things I need to work on.

• ....

• ....

Things I am good at.

• ....

• ....

Things I need to work on.

• ....

• ....

SCOPE-AND-SEQUENCE TABLE BOOK 1

Skill	Minute
Alphabetical order using the first letter	1
Alphabetical order using the second letter	2
Alphabetical order practice	3
Beginning a sentence	4
Ending a sentence	5
Complete sentences	6
Sentence word order	7
Types of sentences	8
Naming parts of sentences	9
Telling parts of sentences	10
Alphabetical order review	11
Beginning and ending a sentence review	12
Sentences review	13
Naming and telling parts of sentences review	14
Naming words for people	15
Naming words for places	16
Naming words for things	17
Naming words for animals	18
Proper names for people	19
Proper names for places	20
Proper names for animals	21
Other proper names (days, months, holidays)	22
Commas (lists)	23
Commas (places)	24
Naming words review	25
More naming words review	26
Proper names review	27
Commas review	28
Action words	29
More on action words	30
Present tense action words	31
Past tense action words	32
Linking verbs (is, are, am)	33
Linking verbs (was, were)	34
Linking verbs (have, has, had)	35
Plural naming words (-s)	36
Plural naming words (-es)	37
More plural naming words (-s, -es)	38
Action words review	39
Present and past tense review	40
Linking verbs review	41
Plural naming words review	42
Pronouns (I, me)	43
Pronouns (she, her)	44
Pronouns (he, him)	45
Pronouns (they, them)	46
Pronouns (we, us)	47
Describing words (size and shape)	48
Describing words (colours and numbers)	49
Describing words (taste and smell)	50
Describing words (touch and sound)	51
Describing words that compare (-er)	52
Describing words that compare (-est)	53
Pronouns review	54
More pronouns review	55
Describing words review	56
Describing words that compare review	57
Nouns that show ownership ('s)	58
More nouns that show ownership ('s)	59
Noun and verb agreement	60
More noun and verb agreement	61
Irregular plural nouns	62
More irregular plural nouns	63
Irregular verbs	64
More irregular verbs	65
Articles (a, an)	66
Articles (a, an, the)	67
Nouns that show ownership review	68
Noun and verb agreement review	69
Irregular plural nouns and verbs review	70
Articles review	71
Compound words	72
More compound words	73
Contractions with not	74
Contractions with to be	75
Synonyms	76
More synonyms	77
Antonyms	78
More antonyms	79
Homophones	80
More homophones	81
Compound words review	82
Contractions review	83
Synonyms and antonyms review	84
Homophones review	85
Apply your grammar knowledge	86–100

Minute 1

Name: .... **Date:** ....

Put the words in the box in alphabetical order.
Write the words on the lines.

tap	rap	cap	map	zap	nap
lap		sap		gap	yap

1. ....

2. ....

3. ....

4. ....

5. ....

6. ....

7. ....

8. ....

9. ....

10. ....

My score: $\dfrac{}{10}$

My time: ....
                     minutes   seconds

Minute 2

Name: .... **Date:** ....

Put each set of words in alphabetical order.

gap	go	get

1. ....

2. ....

3. ....

can	cut	cot

4. ....

5. ....

6. ....

bed	bug	bat	bit

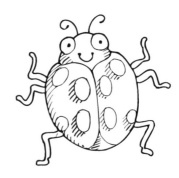

7. ....

8. ....

9. ....

10. ....

My score: $\dfrac{}{10}$ **My time:** ....
        minutes   seconds

Minute 3

Name: .... **Date:** ....

Circle Yes if each set of words is in alphabetical order or No if it is not.

1.	at	mat	sat	Yes	No
2.	bad	sad	mad	Yes	No
3.	ant	ox	bug	Yes	No
4.	ball	cat	gas	Yes	No
5.	jam	run	sun	Yes	No
6.	sat	at	bat	Yes	No
7.	car	fox	ten	Yes	No
8.	top	dog	pan	Yes	No
9.	pen	pan	pot	Yes	No
10.	cap	cot	cut	Yes	No

My score: $\dfrac{}{10}$

My time: ....
minutes   seconds

Minute 4

Name: .... **Date:** ....

Choose the correct word to write at the beginning of each sentence. Write it on the line.

1. .... cat's name is Tabby.
   my   My

2. .... am going to the park.
   I   i

3. .... flower smells sweet.
   The   the

4. .... cleans her room.
   Susan   susan

5. .... likes the colour purple.
   He   he

6. .... are in the tree.
   birds   Birds

7. .... is your mother?
   how   How

8. .... eats a snack.
   she   She

9. .... are not good for your teeth.
   Sweets   sweets

10. .... can write his name.
    danny   Danny

My score: $\dfrac{\quad}{10}$ **My time:** ....
                                                    minutes   seconds

Minute 5

Name: .... **Date:** ....

Choose the correct punctuation mark for the ending of each sentence. Write it on the line.
(**Hint**: A full stop (.) = a telling sentence; a question mark (**?**) = an asking sentence; and an exclamation mark (**!**) = an exclaiming sentence.)

1. The dog is loud ....   ?   !

2. How are you ....   ?   !

3. Maria got a doll ....   ?   !

4. I won a bike ....   ?   !

5. Where is he ....   ?   !

6. Joe likes dogs ....   ?   !

7. Get off the desk ....   ?   !

8. I am at school ....   ?   !

9. Where is my book ....   ?   !

10. May I go now ....   ?   !

My score: $\dfrac{}{10}$

My time: ....
minutes   seconds

Minute 6

Name: .... **Date:** ....

*Read each group of words. Circle **Complete** if each group of words is a complete sentence or **Not complete** if it is not.*

(**Hint**: A sentence tells a complete idea and has a naming part and a telling part.)

1. The dog is black.	Complete	Not complete
2. The boy.	Complete	Not complete
3. The water is cold.	Complete	Not complete
4. Jumps on the bed.	Complete	Not complete
5. My dad and I go fishing.	Complete	Not complete
6. Anthony likes comic books.	Complete	Not complete
7. Running around the tree.	Complete	Not complete
8. Madison bakes cookies.	Complete	Not complete
9. The girl picks red flowers.	Complete	Not complete
10. The zebra at the zoo.	Complete	Not complete

My score: $\dfrac{}{10}$

My time: ....
minutes   seconds

www.prim-ed.com — Prim-Ed Publishing®

Minute 7

Name: .... **Date:** ....

Read each pair of sentences. Circle the correct sentence in each pair.

1. (a) The clouds are fluffy.
   (b) Clouds are the fluffy.

2. (a) Sky is dark the.
   (b) The sky is dark.

3. (a) The came down rain.
   (b) The rain came down.

4. (a) Need water my flowers.
   (b) My flowers need water.

5. (a) She plays in the rain.
   (b) Plays in the rain she.

6. (a) Rainbows I see like to.
   (b) I like to see rainbows.

7. (a) My reads mum a book.
   (b) My mum reads a book.

8. (a) We played board games.
   (b) Games we played board.

9. (a) Red our dog scared was.
   (b) Our red dog was scared.

10. (a) It was a fun day.
    (b) Was a fun day it.

  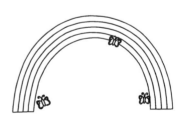

My score: ─────
10

My time: ....
minutes   seconds

Minute 8

Name: .... **Date:** ....

Read each sentence and circle the type of sentence it is.
*Circle **T** for telling, **A** for asking or **E** for exclaiming.*

1. The apples on the tree are red.   T   A   E

2. Can we please have pizza?   T   A   E

3. Where is the party?   T   A   E

4. That is great news!   T   A   E

5. I like reptiles.   T   A   E

6. Sit down now!   T   A   E

7. The police officer was nice.   T   A   E

8. Are we going to the zoo?   T   A   E

9. I broke the jar!   T   A   E

10. I am six years old.   T   A   E

My score: $\dfrac{}{10}$ **My time:** ....
                                                          minutes   seconds

Minute 9

Name: .... **Date:** ....

Circle the naming part in each sentence.
(**Hint**: The naming part of a sentence tells who or what the sentence is about.)

1. The circus was fun.
   The circus   was fun.

2. Lucy and Cindy are twins.
   Lucy and Cindy   are twins.

3. My mother is the best cook.
   My mother   is the best cook.

4. John wants a sandwich.
   John   wants a sandwich.

5. The boy waits for his turn.
   The boy   waits for his turn.

6. Spiders scare the little girl.
   Spiders   scare the little girl.

7. The clouds are fluffy.
   The clouds   are fluffy.

8. Mackenzie and Kaylin are friends.
   Mackenzie and Kaylin   are friends.

9. I like to watch television.
   I   like to watch television.

10. The birds are hungry.
    The birds   are hungry.

My score: ____
10

My time: ....
minutes   seconds

Minute 10

Name: .... **Date:** ....

Circle the telling part in each sentence.

(**Hint**: The telling part of a sentence tells what someone or something does.)

1. My family works in the garden.
   My family   works in the garden.

2. My brother rakes the leaves.
   My brother   rakes the leaves.

3. My mother watches us play.
   My mother   watches us play.

4. I jump into the leaves.
   I   jump into the leaves.

5. Our dog chases me.
   Our dog   chases me.

6. My sister picks up rubbish.
   My sister   picks up rubbish.

7. My father mows the lawn.
   My father   mows the lawn.

8. My mother makes lunch.
   My mother   makes lunch.

9. We eat when we are done.
   We   eat when we are done.

10. The garden looks nice.
    The garden   looks nice.

My score: _____
                10

My time: ....
                minutes   seconds

Name: .... **Date:** ....

Put the words in the box in alphabetical order.
Write the words on the lines.

ox	bug	cat	fish	pig	fox
duck		ant	bird		dog

1. ....

2. ....

3. ....

4. ....

5. ....

6. ....

7. ....

8. ....

9. ....

10. ....

My score: $\dfrac{}{10}$

My time: ....
minutes   seconds

Minute 12

Name: .... **Date:** ....

For Questions 1–5, read each pair of sentences.
Circle the correct sentence in each pair.

1. (a) Meg likes ice-cream.
   (b) meg likes ice-cream.

2. (a) i gave my dog a bath.
   (b) I gave my dog a bath.

3. (a) Bobby plays at school.
   (b) bobby plays at school.

4. (a) Mason beats on his drum.
   (b) mason beats on his drum.

5. (a) brandon likes oranges.
   (b) Brandon likes oranges.

For Questions 6–10, circle the correct punctuation mark for the ending of each sentence. Write it on the line.

6. Watch out for the snake ....   ?   !

7. I do not like snakes ....   ?   !

8. Do you like snakes ....   ?   !

9. My brother thinks snakes are cool ....   ?   !

10. May we look at another animal ....   ?   !

My score: ____ / **10**

My time: .... / ....
minutes   seconds

Minute 13

Name: .... Date: ....

For Questions 1–4, circle Complete *if each group of words is a complete sentence* or Not complete *if it is not*.

1. Feeds the cat.   Complete   Not complete

2. Cary loves to paint.   Complete   Not complete

3. Ji-song catches the ball.   Complete   Not complete

4. Cleaning my room.   Complete   Not complete

For Questions 5–7, rewrite the sentences in the correct word order.

5. kitten my white is.   ....

6. to read like I stories.   ....

7. teacher is our funny.   ....

For Questions 8–10, read each sentence and circle the type of sentence it is. Circle T for telling, A for asking or E for exclaiming.

8. Are you happy?   T   A   E

9. I am excited about my birthday!   T   A   E

10. My parents are very nice.   T   A   E

My score: —— / 10   My time: ....
                              minutes   seconds

Name: .... Date: ....

For Questions 1–5, circle the naming part in each sentence.
(**Hint**: Remember that the naming part of a sentence tells who or what the sentence is about.)

1. Chris has piano practice.
   Chris   has piano practice.

2. The candle is hot.
   The candle   is hot.

3. The bat hangs upside down.
   The bat   hangs upside down.

4. My parents are happy.
   My parents   are happy.

5. Mr Barton gave a test.
   Mr Barton   gave a test.

For Questions 6–10, circle the telling part in each sentence.
(**Hint**: Remember that the telling part of a sentence tells what someone or something does.)

6. My dog chases the cat.
   My dog   chases the cat.

7. The rabbit hops away.
   The rabbit   hops away.

8. The butterfly sits on the flower.
   The butterfly   sits on the flower.

9. The man tells funny stories.
   The man   tells funny stories.

10. My friendly frog jumps up.
    My friendly frog   jumps up.

My score: ____
10

My time: ....
                minutes   seconds

Minute 15

Name: .... **Date:** ....

Circle the naming word for a person in each sentence.

(**Hint**: Each sentence only has one naming word [noun] for a person.)

1. Nia likes to read.
   Nia   likes   to   read.

2. The baby is little.
   The   baby   is   little.

3. My teacher is pretty.
   My   teacher   is   pretty.

4. Ryan plays games.
   Ryan   plays   games.

5. The woman drives fast.
   The   woman   drives   fast.

6. My father cooks dinner.
   My   father   cooks   dinner.

7. Sarah bakes cookies.
   Sarah   bakes   cookies.

8. The postman brings letters.
   The   postman   brings   letters.

9. The zookeeper loves her job.
   The   zookeeper   loves   her   job.

10. Shawn says hello.
    Shawn   says   hello.

My score: $\dfrac{}{10}$ **My time:** ....
                                              minutes   seconds

Minute 16

Name: .... Date: ....

Circle the naming word for a place in each sentence.
(**Hint**: Each sentence only has one naming word [noun] for a place.)

1. Our school is big.
   Our   school   is   big.

2. The classroom has windows.
   The   classroom   has   windows.

3. The library has many books.
   The   library   has   many   books.

4. We eat lunch in the cafe.
   We   eat   lunch   in   the   cafe.

5. The bathroom is clean.
   The   bathroom   is   clean.

6. We play games outside.
   We   play   games   outside.

7. I skip on the playground.
   I   skip   on   the   playground.

8. The nurse has an office.
   The   nurse   has   an   office.

9. We walk across the park.
   We   walk   across   the   park.

10. We shop at that store.
    We   shop   at   that   store.

My score: __ / 10

My time: ....
                    minutes   seconds

Minute 17

Name: .... Date: ....

Circle the naming word for a thing in each sentence.

(**Hint**: Each sentence only has one naming word [noun] for a thing.)

1. The children use crayons to draw.
   The   children   use   crayons   to   draw.

2. That story was too scary!
   That   story   was   too   scary!

3. Hang up your coat.
   Hang   up   your   coat.

4. Ashley drinks milk every day.
   Ashley   drinks   milk   every   day.

5. Take out your scissors.
   Take   out   your   scissors.

6. The clock is round.
   The   clock   is   round.

7. Where is your homework?
   Where   is   your   homework?

8. Alex puts his money away.
   Alex   puts   his   money   away.

9. This dress is my favourite.
   This   dress   is   my   favourite.

10. I write on the paper.
    I   write   on   the   paper.

My score: $\dfrac{\quad}{10}$

My time: ....
                      minutes   seconds

Minute 18

Name: .... **Date:** ....

For Questions 1–5, circle the naming word for an animal in each sentence.

1. The birds are yellow.
   The   birds   are   yellow.

2. This is my sister's cat.
   This   is   my   sister's   cat.

3. The fish swims in the river.
   The   fish   swims   in   the   river.

4. My dog runs and plays.
   My   dog   runs   and   plays.

5. We saw monkeys at the zoo.
   We   saw   monkeys   at   the   zoo.

For Questions 6–10, read each set of words.
Circle the naming word for an animal in each set.

6. farmer	grass	cow	barn
7. ocean	shark	water	boat
8. zoo	cage	zookeeper	lion
9. kennel	puppy	bone	bowl
10. desert	sand	camel	hot

My score: ──── / **10**

My time: ....
                       minutes   seconds

Minute 19

Name: .... **Date:** ....

For Questions 1–5, read each set of words. Circle the correct way to write the proper name for a person in each set.
(**Hint**: Proper names [proper nouns] name special places, people, titles and animals.)

1. ms watson   Ms watson   Ms Watson

2. debra hill   Debra Hill   debra Hill

3. dr young   dr Young   Dr Young

4. Uncle Max   uncle Max   uncle max

5. officer jones   Officer Jones   officer Jones

For Questions 6–10, rewrite each proper name for a person correctly on the line.

6. mike chan   ....

7. miss jenkins   ....

8. mrs patrick   ....

9. aunt meg   ....

10. grandfather joe   ....

My score: $\dfrac{}{10}$

My time: ....
minutes   seconds

Name: .... **Date:** ....

For Questions 1–5, circle the proper name for a place in each sentence.

(**Hint**: Each proper name [proper noun] has two words in it.)

1. My family went to Stone Park.

2. We live on Stirling Street.

3. I go to Dubbo Primary.

4. May we go to Simple Salad for lunch?

5. Mike shops at Jeans Now.

For Questions 6–10, rewrite each proper name for a place correctly on the line.

6. manchester ....

7. united kingdom ....

8. dublin airport ....

9. ocean world ....

10. chinatown ....

My score: ___
$\overline{10}$

My time: ....
minutes   seconds

Minute 21

Name: .... **Date:** ....

Circle the proper name for an animal in each sentence.

1. We saw Ming, the panda.

2. Oscar is five years old.

3. Our class hamster is named Roxy.

4. Kate's favourite whale is Shimmer.

5. His snake, Venom, is huge.

6. May we take Duke for a walk?

7. Her rabbit, Fluffy, is white and black.

8. My dog, Muffin, is scared of noises.

9. We call our goldfish Simon.

10. The puppy's name will be Nella.

My score: $\dfrac{}{10}$ **My time:** ....
                                                    minutes   seconds

Other proper names (days, months, holidays)

Name: .... **Date:** ....

Circle the proper name in each sentence that should begin with a capital letter. Write it correctly on the line.

(**Hint**: These proper names are for days, months and holidays. Each sentence has one proper name that should begin with a capital letter.)

1. We play on saturday. ....

2. My birthday is in june. ....

3. Michelle likes easter the best. ....

4. We see fireworks on new year's Eve. ....

5. We go back to school in september. ....

6. The party is this friday. ....

7. My favourite day is valentine's Day. ....

8. Today is 9, october 2013. ....

9. Bill goes to the library on tuesday. ....

10. She was born on 16, april 1999. ....

My score: _____

10

My time: ....
....
minutes   seconds

Minute 23

Name: .... **Date:** ....

For Questions 1–5, write the comma that is missing in each list.
(**Hint:** A comma separates the different things in a list.)

1. Our dog ran on Monday Wednesday and Saturday.

2. Would you like chocolate strawberry or vanilla ice-cream?

3. Samantha likes apples grapes and bananas.

4. Tennis netball and squash are her favourite sports.

5. Does Bruce prefer lettuce carrots or potatoes?

For Questions 6–10, circle Yes if the comma in the list is correct or No if it is not.

6. Michelle has, a dog a cat and a chicken.   Yes   No

7. Does Nanna arrive on Monday Tuesday,   Yes   No
   or Wednesday?

8. Sport, maths and science are her   Yes   No
   favourite subjects.

9. Please pass the salt, pepper and sauce.   Yes   No

10. Chris, would like red blue and yellow socks. Yes   No

My score: $\frac{}{10}$ **My time:** ....
                                               minutes   seconds

Minute 24

Name: .... Date: ....

For Questions 1–5, write in the comma that is missing in each sentence.
(**Hint**: A comma belongs between the name of a city and its country.)

1. Jessie is from Paris France.

2. Aymee was in Madrid Spain.

3. Ashley lives in Dublin Ireland.

4. We will stop at London England.

5. Where is Lima Peru?

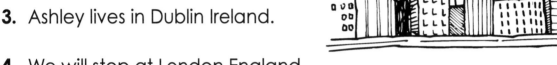

For Questions 6–10, circle the correct way to write the name of each place.
(**Hint**: The names of cities and countries are proper names, and must begin with capital letters.)

6. Bogota, colombia   Bogota, Colombia

7. Tokyo, Japan   tokyo, japan

8. cairo, Egypt   Cairo, Egypt

9. Wellington, New Zealand   Wellington, new Zealand

10. Buenos Aires, Argentina   Buenos aires, Argentina

My score: ____
10

My time: ....
minutes   seconds

Minute 25

Name: .... **Date:** ....

Circle the naming words (nouns) in the sentences.
(**Hint:** Remember that a noun can name a person, place, thing or animal. Each sentence has two nouns.)

1. Apples and bananas taste good.

2. The girl has two sisters.

3. The pupils walk to the playground.

4. My friend rides her bike fast.

5. Our class is at the library.

6. The desks and chairs are wet.

7. The cat sleeps on the rug.

8. The flowers are in the garden.

9. The torch shines in the room.

10. There was food at the party.

My score: —— **My time:** ....
10   minutes   seconds

Commas (places)

Minute 26

Name: .... **Date:** ....

Each word in bold is a noun. Circle what each noun names.

1. **car**	Person	Place	Thing	Animal
2. **school**	Person	Place	Thing	Animal
3. **mum**	Person	Place	Thing	Animal
4. **home**	Person	Place	Thing	Animal
5. **cat**	Person	Place	Thing	Animal
6. **child**	Person	Place	Thing	Animal
7. **plate**	Person	Place	Thing	Animal
8. **bird**	Person	Place	Thing	Animal
9. **doctor**	Person	Place	Thing	Animal
10. **fox**	Person	Place	Thing	Animal

My score: $\dfrac{\quad}{10}$

My time: ....
minutes   seconds

www.prim-ed.com   Prim-Ed Publishing®

Minute 27

Name: .... **Date:** ....

Circle the proper name in each sentence that is missing a capital letter. Rewrite it correctly on the line.

1. Aurelie is from france.   ....

2. Amy and john go to school.   ....

3. Ed's birthday is in february.   ....

4. Lucy reads on saturday.   ....

5. I got chocolate at easter.   ....

6. maria rides her bike.   ....

7. Dr carter helps me.   ....

8. choco the cat is my pet.   ....

9. School is closed on monday.   ....

10. We shop at the melville Centre.   ....

My score: $\dfrac{}{10}$ **My time:** ....
                                                        minutes   seconds

Minute 28

Name: .... **Date:** ....

For Questions 1–5, write in the missing comma in the list in each sentence.

1. Can Emma Liz and Ben come to the park?

2. We need pens pencils and paper.

3. Would you like cake ice-cream or a doughnut?

4. Chicago Miami and New York are my favourite cities.

5. Invite Geraldine Diane and Jennifer.

For Questions 6–10, write in the missing comma in the name of each place.

6. Vancouver Canada

7. Sydney Australia

8. Nairobi Kenya

9. Mexico City Mexico

10. Pretoria South Africa

My score: ___
10

My time: ....
minutes   seconds

Minute 29

Name: .... **Date:** ....

Circle the action word in each sentence.
(**Hint**: Action words [verbs] tell what someone or something does.
Each sentence has one action word.)

1. Bobbi sings in the play.

2. Sally reads a letter.

3. Tony and Carl play tennis.

4. The pupils say hi to me.

5. The plant grows fast.

6. I give letters to my friends.

7. The kids swim in the lake.

8. The sun rises in the east.

9. Dorothy skips on the rug.

10. Meg picks a flower.

My score: —— **My time:** ....
10   minutes   seconds

Minute 30

Name: .... **Date:** ....

For Questions 1–5, choose an action word from the box to complete each sentence. Use each word only once.

1. My sister and I .... with our hands.

2. I .... my mum and dad.

3. The leaves .... from the tree.

4. I .... him with his homework.

5. The frog .... on the log.

fall
help
love
jumps
clap

For Questions 6–10, circle the correct action word to complete each sentence.

6. The birds .... high in the sky.
   fly   jump

7. They .... at the table.
   eat   sleep

8. The wind .... the leaves.
   likes   blows

9. We .... chocolate biscuits.
   make   sing

10. We can't .... in the library.
    read   run

My score: $\dfrac{}{10}$ **My time:** ....
                                              minutes   seconds

www.prim-ed.com   Prim-Ed Publishing®

Minute 31

Name: .... **Date:** ....

Choose the correct action word to complete each sentence. Write it on the line.

(**Hint**: Each sentence tells about something that happens now.)

1. The little boy .... his dog.
   pets   pet

2. My mother .... carrots.
   chop   chops

3. The baker .... lots of cakes.
   bake   bakes

4. Pablo .... lots of pictures.
   paints   paint

5. The big cat .... the mouse.
   chase   chases

6. Sam .... in the sand.
   plays   play

7. Carly .... a castle.
   make   makes

8. The mouse .... up the tree.
   runs   run

9. The tiger .... its paws.
   licks   lick

10. My dog .... at the cars.
    bark   barks

My score: ___
10

My time: ....
              minutes   seconds

Name: .... **Date:** ....

For Questions 1–5, use an action word from the box to complete each sentence. Use each word only once.
(**Hint**: Each sentence tells about something that happened in the past. Many action words add -ed to show that something happened in the past.)

1. The puppy .... with his toy.

2. The rose .... sweet.

3. He .... his tooth out.

4. I .... the film yesterday.

5. Lea .... onto the bed.

pulled

watched

jumped

smelled

played

For Questions 6–10, use an action word from the box to complete each sentence. Use each word only one time.

6. We .... hot dogs and steaks.

7. I .... a question.

8. She .... for the book.

9. I .... my hamster Harry.

10. My mum .... the wall red.

painted

looked

asked

named

cooked

My score: $\dfrac{\quad}{10}$

My time: ....
                                   minutes   seconds

Minute 33

Name: .... **Date:** ....

Write the correct verb (is, are or am) to complete each sentence.

1. I .... happy to be here.
   is   are   am

2. .... we the winners?
   Is   Are   Am

3. The big race .... today.
   is   are   am

4. Nancy and Gina .... happy girls.
   is   are   am

5. They .... home now.
   is   are   am

6. I .... in the school play.
   is   are   am

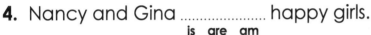

7. The dog's leg .... hurt.
   is   are   am

8. We .... a good class.
   is   are   am

9. Apples .... my favourite fruit.
   is   are   am

10. The weather .... cold today.
    is   are   am

My score: $\dfrac{}{10}$ **My time:** ....
minutes   seconds

Linking verbs (was, were)

Name: .... **Date:** ....

Write the correct verb (was or were) to complete each sentence.

1. I .... with my friends.
   was   were

2. Four ducks .... in the pond.
   was   were

3. The jar .... on the table.
   was   were

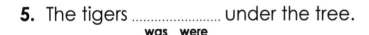

4. The box .... full of gifts.
   was   were

5. The tigers .... under the tree.
   was   were

6. His boat .... blue and green.
   was   were

7. Tom and Jerry .... hot in the sun.
   was   were

8. Last year, she .... not tall.
   was   were

9. The stars .... pretty in the sky.
   was   were

10. My hair .... cut yesterday.
    was   were

My score: ───── **My time:** ....
    10   minutes   seconds

Minute 35

Name: .... **Date:** ....

Circle Yes if the correct verb (have, has or had) is used or No if it is not.

1. I <u>has</u> no more biscuits.   Yes   No

2. Erin <u>had</u> a hat on yesterday.   Yes   No

3. The birds <u>have</u> a worm to eat.   Yes   No

4. They <u>have</u> a football match today.   Yes   No

5. The puppy <u>have</u> big paws.   Yes   No

6. Last week, he <u>has</u> two tests.   Yes   No

7. Bob <u>has</u> a sore throat last night.   Yes   No

8. The baby <u>has</u> one tooth.   Yes   No

9. The cat <u>has</u> a lot of fur.   Yes   No

10. I <u>have</u> two pink dresses.   Yes   No

My score: $\dfrac{\quad}{10}$ **My time:** ....

                                    minutes   seconds

Minute 36

Name: .... **Date:** ....

For Questions 1–5, read each pair of words. Circle the correct naming word that names more than one.

1. car   cars

2. song   songs

3. beds   bed

4. pets   pet

5. aeroplane   aeroplanes

For Questions 6–10, write each naming word to show more than one.

6. street   ....

7. bug   ....

8. book   ....

9. game   ....

10. tree   ....

My score: _____ / **10**

My time: ....
          minutes   seconds

Minute 37

Name: .... **Date:** ....

For Questions 1–6, read each pair of words. Circle the correct naming word that names more than one.

1. fox   foxes

2. dishes   dish

3. couch   couches

4. bush   bushes

5. glasses   glass

6. bus   buses

For Questions 7–10, circle the naming word that names more than one in each sentence.

7. Sam has three watches.

8. These boxes are light.

9. The beaches in Spain are big.

10. Four classes went on the school excursion.

My score: ────
10

My time: ....
                minutes   seconds

Name: .... **Date:** ....

For Questions 1–5, read each set of words. Circle the correct naming word that names more than one in each set.

1. hills   hilles   hill

2. peaches   peach   peachs

3. circus   circuses   circuss

4. spoons   spoon   spoones

5. wishes   wishs   wish

For Questions 6–10, rewrite each naming word to show more than one.

6. hand   ....

7. box   ....

8. coin   ....

9. branch   ....

10. bird   ....

My score: $\dfrac{\qquad}{10}$ **My time:** ....
minutes   seconds

Minute 39

Name: .... **Date:** ....

Circle the action word in each sentence.

1. We eat hot dogs for lunch.

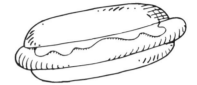

2. I pet my dog on the head.

3. My dad paints the house.

4. We ran in the race.

5. The tree grew tall.

6. I went to the shop.

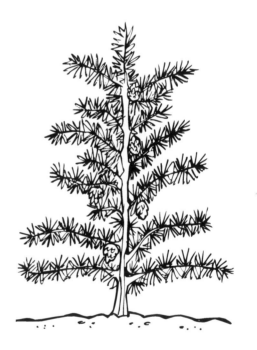

7. The ice melted in the sun.

8. We go to that park.

9. The band walked on the field.

10. My mum takes me to the park.

My score: $\dfrac{}{10}$ **My time:** ....
minutes   seconds

Present and past tense review

Name: .... **Date:** ....

Circle whether each sentence is in the Present or in the Past.
(**Hint**: When something happens now, it is *present*. When something happened already, it is *past*.)

1. They fished in the lake yesterday.   Present   Past

2. Susan listens to the teacher.   Present   Past

3. I know all about whales.   Present   Past

4. Regina helped her dad clean.   Present   Past

5. Simon runs faster than everyone.   Present   Past

6. Our kitten likes fresh milk.   Present   Past

7. I kicked the ball in the air.   Present   Past

8. We called Grandma Rose last night.   Present   Past

9. The pupils ride on a bus.   Present   Past

10. Joey wanted a bike last Christmas.   Present   Past

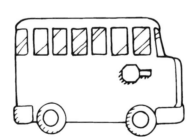

My score: —— / **10**

My time: ....
                    minutes   seconds

www.prim-ed.com   Prim-Ed Publishing®

Minute 41

Name: .... **Date:** ....

For Questions 1–5, use a verb from the box to complete each sentence. Use each word only one time.

1. Lisa .... two eggs for breakfast.

2. We .... with my dad yesterday.

3. Joey .... in a music lesson.

4. I .... seven years old today.

5. Why .... you mad at me?

is
are
am
were
had

For Questions 6–10, write the correct verb to complete each sentence.

6. Where .... my coat?
   is   are

7. We .... a party last Halloween.
   had   has

8. Do you .... a pen for me?
   has   have

9. The wind .... cold last night.
   were   was

10. Molly .... two best friends.
    have   has

My score: $\dfrac{\quad}{10}$

My time: ....
        minutes   seconds

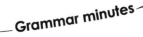

Minute 42

Name: .... Date: ....

For Questions 1–5, read each pair of words.
Circle the correct noun that names more than one.

1. cows   cowes

2. cupes   cups

3. witches   witchs

4. pailes   pails

5. foxes   foxs

For Questions 6–10, write the correct noun to complete each sentence.

6. Her brother has five red ....
   hates   hats

7. They have two baby ....
   girls   girl

8. Our new...........................are very nice.
   dishes   dish

9. These .... sell toys.
   shop   shops

10. I made three .... for my birthday.
    wishs   wishes

My score: ———
         10

My time: ....
              minutes   seconds

Minute 43

Name: .... **Date:** ....

Write I or me *to complete each sentence.*
(**Hint:** *I* is used in the naming part of a sentence, and *me* is used in the telling part of a sentence.)

1. .... am a fast runner.

2. My mum gives .... a snack every day.

3. Will you take .... to the shop?

4. .... am very sleepy.

5. My baby sister loves ....

6. Am .... going with you?

7. He told .... a funny story.

8. .... am not cold.

9. Why am .... so tall?

10. My friend, Jen, wrote .... a letter.

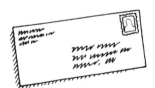

My score: $\dfrac{}{10}$

My time: ....
minutes   seconds

Minute 44

Name: .... **Date:** ....

For Questions 1–5, write she or her *to complete each sentence.*
(**Hint**: *She* and *her* take the place of a naming word for a girl or a woman. *She* is used in the naming part of a sentence, and *her* is used in the telling part of a sentence.)

1. I saw .... eat the glue!

2. I want to give .... flowers.

3. .... is going to school.

4. Is .... in bed yet?

5. I read my poem to ....

For Questions 6–10, circle she or her to take the place of the underlined words.

6. <u>Anne</u> paints pretty pictures.
   She   Her

7. I made <u>my mum</u> a birthday card.
   she   her

8. <u>Our teacher</u> knows a lot of things.
   She   Her

9. Tom let <u>Lisa</u> use his pen.
   she   her

10. Do you like <u>the new girl in class</u>?
    she   her

My score: _____
10

My time: ....
minutes   seconds

www.prim-ed.com   Prim-Ed Publishing®

Minute 45

Name: .... **Date:** ....

For Questions 1–5, circle he or him *to take the place of the underlined words.*

(**Hint:** *He* and *him* take the place of a naming word for a boy or a man. *He* is used in the naming part of a sentence and *him* is used in the telling part of a sentence.)

1. <u>The man</u> sleeps on the couch.
   He   Him

2. <u>Harry</u> likes to play in the snow.
   He   Him

3. I can ride my bike faster than <u>Phil</u>.
   he   him

4. The teacher is looking at <u>Jack</u>.
   he   him

5. <u>The policeman</u> helps people.
   He   Him

For Questions 6–10, read the first sentence and then write he or him *to complete the second sentence.*

6. My dad works at a school. .... is a teacher.

7. I saw John yesterday. I played cards with ....

8. His brother plays football. .... is strong!

9. That man eats a lot. .... is always hungry.

10. Matt is in my class. I sit near ....

My score: $\dfrac{\quad}{10}$ **My time:** ....
                                                              minutes   seconds

Minute 46

Name: .... **Date:** ....

For Questions 1–5, circle They or Them *to take the place of the underlined words.*

(**Hint:** *They* is used in the naming part of a sentence and *them* is used in the telling part of a sentence.)

1. <u>Her gifts</u> are on the desk.   They   Them

2. <u>The girls</u> like to run around the lake.   They   Them

3. We saw <u>his mum and dad</u> outside.   they   them

4. <u>Luke and Tim</u> are going to the Easter Show.   They   Them

5. Susie says hello to <u>her friends</u>.   they   them

For Questions 6–10, write they or them *to take the place of the underlined words.*

6. Mrs Hill tells <u>the boys</u> to stop.   ....

7. <u>My grandparents</u> are coming to visit.   ....

8. <u>The birds</u> are in the nest.   ....

9. Pam has <u>her toys</u> at school.   ....

10. <u>The girls</u> talk all day.   ....

My score: _____
10

My time: ....
minutes   seconds

www.prim-ed.com   Prim-Ed Publishing®

Minute 47

Name: .... **Date:** ....

For Questions 1–5, write we or us to complete each sentence.
(**Hint**: *We* is used in the naming part of a sentence and *us* is used in the telling part of a sentence.)

1. .... have a cat and a dog.
   We   Us

2. Why does he yell at ....?
   we   us

3. They are taking .... to the zoo.
   we   us

4. .... know how to count.
   We   Us

5. My mum was with ....
   we   us

For Questions 6–10, circle Yes if the underlined pronoun is used correctly or No if it is not.

6. <u>Us</u> take a bath at night.   Yes   No

7. <u>We</u> write thankyou letters.   Yes   No

8. The teacher tells <u>we</u> a story.   Yes   No

9. Why are <u>us</u> going there?   Yes   No

10. The dog licked <u>us</u> on the face.   Yes   No

My score: $\dfrac{\quad}{10}$ **My time:** ....
                                              minutes   seconds

Minute 48

Name: .... **Date:** ....

For Questions 1–5, write the correct describing word to complete each sentence.
(**Hint**: These describing words [adjectives] tell about size.)

1. The .... baby cried for his mother.
   old   little

2. The .... tree was cut down.
   tall   ugly

3. I like the elephant because it is ....
   big   light

4. The worm is very ....
   long   dirty

5. A .... ant is on my arm.
   black   small

For Questions 6–10, circle the describing word in each sentence.
(**Hint**: These describing words [adjectives] tell about shape.)

6. Sarah has a round pumpkin.

7. The square clock is on the wall.

8. The pancakes we made were flat.

9. My brother has an oval face.

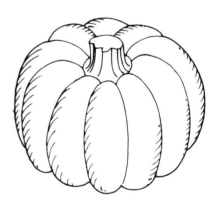

10. These chips are so skinny!

My score: $\dfrac{\quad}{10}$ **My time:** ....
minutes   seconds

Describing words (colours and numbers)

Name: .... **Date:** ....

Circle the describing word in each sentence.

(**Hint**: These describing words [adjectives] tell about colours and numbers.)

1. Her dress was pink.

2. She wore two bows in her hair.

3. The blue bird flies away.

4. The four friends eat pizza.

5. My three children are boys.

6. We both like red apples.

7. The black dog is nice.

8. The yellow stars are in the sky.

9. Please take five types of sweets.

10. The three boys went home.

My score: $\dfrac{\quad}{10}$ **My time:** ....

minutes   seconds

Minute 50

Name: .... **Date:** ....

Circle the describing word in each sentence.

(**Hint**: These describing words [adjectives] tell about taste and smell.)

1. The apple was sweet.

2. The lemon is sour.

3. I don't like spicy crisps.

4. My bedroom smells clean.

5. This gum is minty.

6. Our dinner was yummy.

7. Grapes are a tasty treat.

8. Those eggs must be rotten!

9. I like to eat creamy soups.

10. My dog is so stinky!

My score: $\dfrac{}{10}$ **My time:** ....
                                                      minutos   seconds

Name: .... **Date:** ....

Circle the describing word in each sentence.

(**Hint**: These describing words [adjectives] tell about touch and sound.)

1. My soft cat is named Bella.

2. His loud snoring woke everyone up.

3. I like her fuzzy sweater.

4. The hard ball hit my head.

5. The squeaky door opened.

6. He loves the silky blanket.

7. The squealing pig ate corn.

8. The chirping birds sat in the tree.

9. The rough wood needs sanding.

10. The sharp knife cut him.

My score: $\dfrac{}{10}$

My time: ....
minutes   seconds

Describing words that compare (-er)

Name: .... **Date:** ....

For Questions 1–5, write the describing word that completes each sentence.

(**Hint**: When describing words compare two things, they sometimes end in -er.)

1. Tyra is .... than my brother.
   tall   taller

2. I think maths is .... than science.
   easy   easier

3. Their house is much .... than our house.
   bigger   big

4. It is .... in August than it is in December.
   hotter   hot

5. Our dog is .... than our cat.
   old   older

For Questions 6–10, complete each sentence with the correct describing word.

(**Hint**: Use the underlined word in each sentence to help you figure out the missing word.)

6. My ruler is <u>long</u>, but the teacher's ruler is even ....

7. Last winter was <u>cold</u>, but this winter is much ....

8. I can run <u>fast</u>, but not .... than my friend Luke.

9. Jenna is <u>nice</u> to me, but her sister is even .... to me.

10. A bird flies <u>high</u>, but an aeroplane can go ....

My score: _____
10

My time: ....
minutes   seconds

www.prim-ed.com   Prim-Ed Publishing®

Minute 53

Name: .... **Date:** ....

For Questions 1–5, write the describing word that completes each sentence.
(**Hint**: When describing words compare more than two things, they sometimes end in -est.)

1. Kelly is the .... person in our class.
   stronger   strongest

2. Our dog was the .... dog at the dog park.
   small   smallest

3. My grandad has one of the .... coins in the world.
   oldest   older

4. We all tell funny jokes, but Jim tells the .... jokes of all.
   funniest   funny

5. A writer in Germany wrote the .... sentence ever.
   long   longest

For Questions 6–10, write Yes if the underlined describing word is correct or No if it is not.

6. Nelson has the <u>small</u> apple I have ever seen.   ....

7. Lisa is the <u>smartest</u> person I know.   ....

8. Bart made the <u>bigger</u> mess of all.   ....

9. I read the <u>longest</u> book in the library.   ....

10. Our teacher is the <u>nicest</u> one in the school.   ....

My score: $\dfrac{}{10}$ **My time:** ....
                                   minutes   seconds

Name: .... **Date:** ....

Circle Yes if the underlined pronoun in each sentence is correct or No if it is not.

1. <u>Him</u> has a tennis game today.   Yes   No

2. <u>I</u> always wash the dishes for my mum.   Yes   No

3. Give Don's pencil back to <u>he</u>.   Yes   No

4. Santa gave <u>me</u> a new bike last year.   Yes   No

5. We are asking <u>they</u> to come over.   Yes   No

6. Please help <u>us</u> find the lost kitten.   Yes   No

7. Where are <u>them</u> going?   Yes   No

8. I told my grandma I would call <u>her</u> later.   Yes   No

9. Michael and <u>me</u> go camping all the time.   Yes   No

10. <u>Them</u> are going surfing this Sunday.   Yes   No

My score: $\dfrac{}{10}$ **My time:** ....
     minutes   seconds

Minute 55 ___

Name: .... Date: ....

For Questions 1–5, circle the correct pronoun to take the place of the underlined words.

1. <u>Katie</u> walked her dog to the park.
   She   Her

2. I gave <u>Mel and Liz</u> some of my stickers.
   they   them

3. We saw <u>the clown</u> at the circus.
   he   him

4. My brother made <u>my mum and I</u> sick.
   we   us

5. Jeff said I tripped <u>Jenny</u>, but I didn't.
   she   her

For Questions 6–10, read the first sentence, and then write the correct pronoun missing in the second sentence.

6. Jerry is so smart. .... always gets good marks.
   He   Him

7. The Cruz sisters can sing. .... can also dance.
   They   Them

8. I asked my parents for a pony. They told .... 'No'.
   I   me

9. Dr Smith is nice. We went to see .... yesterday.
   she   her

10. Mrs Potter likes my sister. She gave .... a book.
    she   her

My score: $\dfrac{}{10}$ My time: ....
                                              minutes   seconds

Minute 56

Name: .... **Date:** ....

Circle the describing words in the sentences.
(**Hint**: Each sentence has two describing words [adjectives] to circle.)

1. The tall man ate the spicy chicken.

2. Tommy is wearing dark trousers and big boots.

3. There are red apples in the white basket.

4. The sweet juice is in a tall glass.

5. Kim's warm jacket is furry.

6. The black banana is rotten.

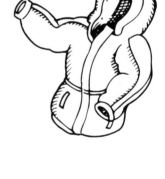

7. I had one banknote and two coins.

8. The square pillow is soft.

9. Lou made a dark chocolate cake.

10. The loud dog barked at the quiet cat.

My score: _____
10

My time: ....
minutes   seconds

www.prim-ed.com   Prim-Ed Publishing®

Minute 57

Name: .... **Date:** ....

For Questions 1–5, write the describing word that completes each sentence.

1. My hair is .... than my sister's hair.
   longer   longest

2. Our tree is the .... one on the street.
   taller   tallest

3. Wendy got to school .... than anyone.
   later   latest

4. That black kitten is the .... of them all.
   cuter   cutest

5. I have the .... desk in the class.
   cleaner   cleanest

For Questions 6–10, read each set of sentences. Write the correct describing word missing in each set.

6. I am tall. He is .... She is the tallest of all.

7. A cat is small. A mouse is smaller. An ant is the .... of all.

8. Apples are sweet. Chocolate is .... Honey is the sweetest of all.

9. He is nice. She is .... I am the nicest of all.

10. The music is loud. That music is louder. This music is the

    ....

My score: $\frac{}{10}$ **My time:** ....
                                        minutes   seconds

Minute 58

Name: .... **Date:** ....

Circle the noun in each sentence that shows ownership.

(**Hint**: An apostrophe and an s ('s) on naming words [nouns] show ownership.)

1. Sally's dog is dirty.

2. The plane's wings are white.

3. The cat's ball of wool is purple.

4. Dean's bike needs a new tyre.

5. Maria's favourite colour is pink.

6. The tree's leaves are yellow.

7. The park's slide is very long.

8. The computer's mouse is lost.

9. The bunny's ears are furry.

10. Becky's family is going to France.

My score: _____
10

My time: ....

minutes   seconds

Minute 59

Name: .... **Date:** ....

For Questions 1–5, write Yes if the underlined noun shows ownership or No if it does not.

1. The <u>bird's</u> feathers were blue. ....

2. My new <u>doll</u> is very tall. ....

3. The <u>tree's</u> branches are thick. ....

4. <u>Robert's</u> coat keeps him warm. ....

5. The <u>clock</u> rang loudly. ....

For Questions 6–10, draw a line to match each group of words on the left with the correct way to show ownership on the right.

6. fur on the cat   (a) shirt's button

7. car that belongs to the man   (b) woman's hat

8. button on the shirt   (c) cat's fur

9. toy that belongs to the girl   (d) man's car

10. hat on the woman   (e) girl's toy

My score: ___
10

My time: ....
        minutes   seconds

Minute 60

Name: .... **Date:** ....

Write the correct verb to complete each sentence.

1. My mum .... my bed.
   make   makes

2. The girl .... in a pretty voice.
   sing   sings

3. The boy .... too loudly.
   talk   talks

4. The dog will .... his tail at his owner.
   wag   wags

5. Fred .... his car.
   wash   washes

6. The birds .... to their nest.
   fly   flies

7. Rachel .... her keys all the time.
   lose   loses

8. Ken .... his bike to work.
   ride   rides

9. The zebras .... through the grass.
   run   runs

10. My dad .... faster than my mum.
    drive   drives

My score: ___
   10

My time: ....
   minutes   seconds

Name: .... **Date:** ....

For Questions 1–5, use the verbs in the box to complete each sentence. Use each word only once.

1. The girls .... each other goodbye.

2. The woman .... on the track every day.

3. Charles .... basketball on Mondays.

4. The children .... lots of cakes at this shop.

5. Karla and Michelle .... biscuits to sell.

plays
buy
runs
bake
hug

For Questions 6–10, write the correct verb to complete each sentence.

6. The baby .... his food on the floor.
   throw   throws

7. Kate .... bubbles with her gum.
   blow   blows

8. Patrick .... along the path.
   skip   skips

9. Steve and John .... books in the library.
   read   reads

10. The spiders .... webs on the barn.
    make   makes

My score: ──── **My time:** ....
       10   minutes   seconds

Minute 62

Name: .... Date: ....

Write the correct noun that names more than one in each sentence.
(**Hint**: These naming words [nouns] change spelling to name more than one.)

1. Five .... cried when they saw the clown.
   childs   children

2. I read a story about .... who help a fairy princess.
   elfs   elves

3. All of the .... ran into the hole.
   mice   mouses

4. The .... swam slowly in the water.
   gooses   geese

5. The dentist took out two of my ....
   teeth   toothes

6. All the .... in my family are tall.
   womans   women

7. The .... are playing with the kids outside.
   men   mans

8. Linda's .... are bigger than my feet.
   feet   foots

9. Many .... like to eat ice-cream.
   peoples   people

10. The .... on the tree turned yellow.
    leaves   leafs

My score: _____
   10

My time: ....
            minutes   seconds

Minute 63

Name: .... **Date:** ....

For Questions 1–5, read each set of words.
Circle the correct noun that names more than one in each set.

1. childs   children   childes

2. shelves   shelfes   shelfs

3. tooths   teeth   teeths

4. life   lifes   lives

5. feet   foots   footes

For Questions 6–10, rewrite each noun to show more than one.

6. man   ....

7. wolf   ....

8. woman   ....

9. goose   ....

10. mouse   ....

My score: $\dfrac{}{10}$ **My time:** ....
                                           minutes   seconds

Minute 64

Name: .... **Date:** ....

Write the correct verb to complete each sentence.

1. I .... the horses at the ranch.

saw   seen

2. Kelly .... the party early.

leaved   left

3. Tom .... the ducks at the pond.

feed   fed

4. I .... a tooth during lunch.

lost   lose

5. Sherry was so thirsty she .... all the water.

drinked   drank

6. The story Kris .... won a prize.

wrote   write

7. Roxy and Bianca .... lunch with their dad.

ate   eated

8. Darren .... out of the tree this afternoon.

fell   fall

9. Holly .... in the deep end of the pool.

swam   swimmed

10. My dad .... slowly in the rain.

drove   drived

My score: ___/**10**

My time: ....

minutes   seconds

Minute 65

Name: .... **Date:** ....

For Questions 1–5, circle the correct past-tense verb in each pair.

1. maked   made

2. wrote   writed

3. fell   falled

4. breaked   broke

5. took   taked

For Questions 6–10, write each verb in the past tense.
(**Hint**: These are irregular verbs, which are verbs that do not add -ed to tell about the past.)

6. see   ....

7. run   ....

8. eat   ....

9. come   ....

10. say   ....

My score: $\dfrac{}{10}$

My time: ....
                          minutes   seconds

Minute 66

Name: .... **Date:** ....

Write a or an *in front of each noun (naming word).*
(**Hint:** Use *a* before words that begin with a consonant sound. Use *an* before words that begin with a vowel sound. The vowels are *a, e, i, o* and *u*.)

1. .... apple

2. .... computer

3. .... glass

4. .... igloo

5. .... egg

6. .... team

7. .... cage

8. .... emu

9. .... umbrella

10. .... table

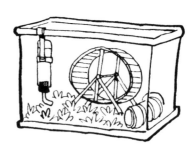

My score: $\dfrac{}{10}$

My time: ....
 minutes   seconds

www.prim-ed.com Prim-Ed Publishing®

Minute 67

Name: .... **Date:** ....

Write a, an *or the to complete each sentence.*
(**Hint**: Remember that sentences must begin with a capital letter.)

1. .... horses are running around the track.

2. .... alligator creeps along the swamp.

3. We are taking .... aeroplane to New Mexico.

4. .... hairdresser on Jones Street cuts my hair.

5. .... ladybird sits on the leaf.

6. Jackie rakes .... leaves into a pile.

7. I can't find .... pencil to use.

8. May I have .... ice-cream?

9. I had pancakes and .... apple for breakfast.

10. .... class is ready for the excursion.

My score: $\dfrac{\quad}{10}$ **My time:** ....
                                                          minutes   seconds

Minute 68

Name: .... **Date:** ....

For Questions 1–5, circle the noun in each sentence that shows ownership.

1. Maggie's writing is not very messy.

2. Carrie's blanket is soft and warm.

3. The girl's tooth fell out this morning.

4. Bob's maths homework is all correct.

5. Our dog's puppies were born last night.

For Questions 6–10, write Yes if the underlined noun shows ownership or No if it does not.

6. The <u>plant</u> leaves are bright green. ....

7. The <u>house's</u> gate is painted white. ....

8. <u>Carol's</u> grandmother is coming to visit. ....

9. The <u>firefighter</u> truck drove by. ....

10. The <u>baby's</u> bottle needs more milk. ....

My score: ___
10

My time: ....
minutes   seconds

Name: .... **Date:** ....

For Questions 1–5, write the correct verb to complete each sentence.

1. Emily .... three laps around the pool.
    swims   swim

2. Heidi .... Emily swim.
    watch   watched

3. Kate and Lea .... to swim, too.
    like   likes

4. All of the girls .... into the pool.
    dive   dives

5. They .... each other in the pool.
    raced   races

For Questions 6–10, use the verbs in the box to complete each sentence. Use each word only one time.

washed	rings	takes	does	wins

6. Lupita always .... when we race.

7. The baby .... a nap every afternoon.

8. My brother and I .... the dishes last night.

9. The phone .... a lot in our house.

10. The new pupil .... the best work he can.

My score: $\dfrac{}{10}$ **My time:** ....
                                                              minutes   seconds

Name: .... **Date:** ....

For Questions 1–5, circle whether each noun names One or More than one.

1. leaves   One   More than one

2. person   One   More than one

3. wolf   One   More than one

4. men   One   More than one

5. knives   One   More than one

For Questions 6–10, circle whether each sentence describes something in the Present (happening now) or in the Past (already happened).

6. I bring my lunch to school.   Present   Past

7. My mum bought that book for me.   Present   Past

8. We all went camping last summer.   Present   Past

9. The film star flies his own plane.   Present   Past

10. I felt sick after I ate that whole cake!   Present   Past

My score: ___ / 10   **My time:** ....
minutes   seconds

Minute 71

Name: .... **Date:** ....

Write Yes *if the underlined article is correct or* **No** *if it is not.*
(**Hint**: *A, an* and *the* are called articles.)

1. <u>An</u> pear is my favourite fruit. ....

2. <u>The</u> shoes hurt my feet. ....

3. We go to <u>the</u> pond near my house to fish. ....

4. <u>A</u> car crashed into a tree. ....

5. Sue is excited about riding <u>an</u> elephant
   at the circus. ....

6. <u>A</u> boots belong to my mother. ....

7. <u>An</u> octopus is swimming nearby. ....

8. I want to go to <u>an</u> national park. ....

9. The little girl eats <u>a</u> slice of apple pie. ....

10. Please don't put <u>an</u> orange in my lunch. ....

My score: $\dfrac{\quad}{10}$ **My time:** ....
minutes   seconds

Name: .... **Date:** ....

Circle the compound word in each sentence.
(**Hint**: A compound word is made up of two words. Each sentence has only one compound word to circle.)

1. I can't find my watch in my bedroom.

2. We have a pool in our backyard.

3. My shoelaces are too short for my shoes.

4. The sunshine felt warm on my skin.

5. We saw jellyfish at the beach.

6. My mother baked homemade bread.

7. Give your teacher your homework.

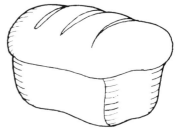

8. My uncle has three grandchildren.

9. I ate eggs and sausages for breakfast.

10. Did you go along the walkway?

My score: $\dfrac{}{10}$

My time: ....
minutes   seconds

Minute 73

Name: .... **Date:** ....

Write Yes if each word is a compound word or No if it is not.

1. songbird ....

2. grass ....

3. slide ....

4. motorway ....

5. seashell ....

6. pencil ....

7. whiteboard ....

8. sailboat ....

9. radio ....

10. rainbow ....

My score: $\dfrac{}{10}$ **My time:** ....

minutes   seconds

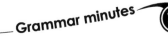

Minute 74

Name: .... **Date:** ....

For Questions 1–5, read each pair of words. Circle the correct contraction in each pair.

(**Hint**: A contraction is a word made when you join two words. But unlike compound words, a contraction uses an apostrophe (') to show where a letter or letters were left out.)

1. isn't   isnt'

2. hasnt   hasn't

3. don't   do'nt

4. ca'nt   can't

5. willn't   won't

For Questions 6–10, use the contractions in the box to complete each sentence. Use each word only once.

shouldn't	haven't	isn't	don't	won't

6. I .... seen that film yet.

7. The pupils .... know how to add.

8. You .... give the little dog a big bone.

9. Sarah .... be seven years old until May.

10. My letter from Aunt Janet .... here yet.

My score: $\frac{\qquad}{10}$ **My time:** ....

minutes   seconds

Minute 75

Name: .... **Date:** ....

For Questions 1–6, draw a line to match each group of words on the left with its correct contraction on the right.

1. I am   (a) you're

2. it is   (b) she's

3. you are   (c) we're

4. they are   (d) I'm

5. she is   (e) it's

6. we are   (f) they're

For Questions 7–10, use the contractions in the box to complete each sentence. Use each word only once.

you're	I'm	we're	she's

7. We get in trouble when .... too loud.

8. Estella, ... the best friend I have.

9. Everyone tells Kasey that .... a good singer.

10. .... getting my new bike today.

My score: $\dfrac{\quad}{10}$ **My time:** ....
                                              minutes   seconds

Minute 76 _____

Name: .... **Date:** ....

For Questions 1–5, circle the correct synonym that goes with each clue.
(**Hint**: A synonym is a word that means the same thing or almost the same thing.)

1. This word means the same as <u>glad</u>.
   happy   sad

2. This word means the same as <u>big</u>.
   little   large

3. This word means the same as <u>beautiful</u>.
   pretty   ugly

4. This word means the same as <u>fast</u>.
   slow   quick

5. This word means the same as <u>yell</u>.
   shout   whisper

For Questions 6–10, draw a line to match the underlined word in each sentence on the left with its correct synonym on the right.

6. All of her answers were <u>correct</u>.   (a)   mad

7. The clown told us <u>funny</u> jokes.   (b)   start

8. The <u>tiny</u> mouse ran through the hole.   (c)   right

9. We will <u>begin</u> the test in five minutes.   (d)   small

10. My mother was <u>angry</u> with me.   (e)   silly

My score: $\dfrac{}{10}$ **My time:** ....
                                                    minutes   seconds

Minute 77

Name: .... **Date:** ....

For Questions 1–6, read each set of words. Circle the two synonyms in each set.

1. hot   warm   cold

2. see   say   look

3. fat   thin   thick

4. sleep   nap   awake

5. kind   mean   nice

6. close   open   shut

For Questions 7–10, read each pair of sentences. Look at the underlined word in the first sentence. Circle its synonym in the second sentence.

7. Our new television is <u>large</u>. It is too big for the room.

8. The rabbit <u>hops</u> all around. He jumps high in the air.

9. I was <u>unhappy</u> when we lost the game. It made me feel sad.

10. Mike <u>enjoys</u> playing cricket. He likes to play all the time.

My score: $\dfrac{}{10}$ **My time:** ....
                                           minutes   seconds

 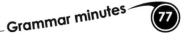

Minute 78

9
8
7
6

Name: .... **Date:** ....

For Questions 1–5, read each pair of words. Write Yes if they are antonyms or No if they are not.
(**Hint**: Antonyms are words that mean the opposite.)

1. slow   fast   ....

2. happy   excited   ....

3. open   close   ....

4. in   inside   ....

5. start   stop   ....

For Questions 6–10, read each set of words. Circle the two antonyms in each set.

6. young   old   child

7. push   tug   pull

8. hard   solid   soft

9. clean   dirty   fresh

10. right   up   left

My score: _____
10

My time: ....
minutes   seconds

Name: .... **Date:** ....

For Questions 1–6, circle the correct antonym for the underlined word in each sentence.

1. Bobby is <u>on</u> the chair.   above   off

2. The <u>fat</u> cat belongs to Casey.   thin   big

3. The dog was <u>wet</u> after his bath.   clean   dry

4. Please <u>close</u> the door.   open   take

5. It was a bright and sunny <u>day</u>.   light   night

6. We <u>start</u> school early in the morning.   end   begin

For Questions 7–10, match each word on the left with its correct antonym on the right.

7. huge   (a)   new

8. fast   (b)   pretty

9. ugly   (c)   tiny

10. old   (d)   slow

My score: $\dfrac{\quad\quad}{10}$ **My time:** ....
                                                            minutes   seconds

Minute 80

Name: .... **Date:** ....

For Questions 1–6, read each pair of words. Write Yes if they sound alike or No if they do not.

(Hint: Homophones are words that sound the same but are spelt differently and have different meanings.)

1. hi   high   ....

2. say   saw   ....

3. son   sun   ....

4. be   bee   ....

5. man   mean   ....

6. to   two   ....

For Questions 7–10, match each word on the left with a word on the right that sounds like it.

7. by   (a) blew

8. ate   (b) see

9. blue   (c) eight

10. sea   (d) buy

My score: $\dfrac{}{10}$ **My time:** ....

                                            minutes   seconds

www.prim-ed.com   Prim-Ed Publishing®

Minute 81

Name: .... **Date:** ....

For Questions 1–5, read each pair of sentences. Circle the homophones in each pair.
(**Hint**: You must circle one word in each sentence.)

1. We wear blue shirts to school. I don't know where we got them.

2. I know the answer to the question. The answer is 'No'.

3. Our dad is great. He comes home in one hour.

4. I can't hear the baby. Bring him here to me.

5. The turtles swim in the sea. I see them every morning.

For Questions 6–10, read each set of words. Circle the two words that sound alike in each set.

6. so   sew   saw

7. knew   knee   new

8. four   fire   for

9. dare   deer   dear

10. meet   might   meat

My score: $\dfrac{}{10}$ **My time:** ....
                                              minutes   seconds

Name: .... **Date:** ....

For Questions 1–5, circle the correct compound word for the two underlined words in each sentence.

1. A <u>fish</u> shaped like a <u>star</u>.   starfish   fishstar

2. A <u>room</u> with a <u>bed</u> in it.   roombed   bedroom

3. A <u>bell</u> for the <u>door</u>.   belldoor   doorbell

4. A <u>house</u> for a <u>dog</u>.   doghouse   housedog

5. A <u>bird</u> that is <u>black</u>.   birdblack   blackbird

For Questions 6–10, write a compound word with two words from each sentence.

6. The ball is made of snow.   ....

7. The boat has a sail.   ....

8. The shine comes from the sun.   ....

9. This lace is for my shoe.   ....

10. I have a pit full of sand.   ....

My score: ____
10

My time: ....
minutos   seconds

Minute 83

Name: .... **Date:** ....

For Questions 1–5, write the two words that make up each contraction.

1. she's   ....

2. we're   ....

3. shouldn't   ....

4. don't   ....

5. I'm   ....

For Questions 6–10, write the contraction to best complete each sentence.

6. Mark said .... not hungry.
                       he's   she's

7. .... eat crisps before dinner.
   Shouldn't   Don't

8. My brother .... read yet.
              can't   isn't

9. The film .... started.
         haven't   hasn't

10. The teacher told us .... good pupils.
                 we're   I'm

My score: $\frac{}{10}$ **My time:** ....
                                               minutes   seconds

Minute 84

Name: .... Date: ....

Write S if the pairs of words are synonyms or A if they are antonyms.

(**Hint**: Remember that synonyms are words that mean the same thing, and antonyms are words that mean the opposite.)

1. on   off   ....

2. happy   excited   ....

3. early   late   ....

4. sad   happy   ....

5. nice   sweet   ....

6. buy   sell   ....

7. easy   hard   ....

8. mad   angry   ....

9. fast   slow   ....

10. tall   high   ....

My score: $\dfrac{}{10}$

My time: ....
         minutes   seconds

www.prim-ed.com   Prim-Ed Publishing®

Minute 85

Name: .... **Date:** ....

Write the correct word to complete each sentence.

1. The eagle .... high in the sky.
   flu   flew

2. I want you to .... my family.
   meat   meet

3. The .... is full of beautiful fish.
   see   sea

4. You have one .... to finish your homework.
   our   hour

5. I .... first place in the contest.
   one   won

6. The mouse ate the .... piece of cheese.
   whole   hole

7. Lana got dirt in her ....
   eye   I

8. His .... lives with his grandma.
   son   sun

9. My dog chases his own ....
   tale   tail

10. .... you like to come with us?
    Would   Wood

My score: ____ / 10   **My time:** ....
                                              minutes   seconds

Minute 86

Name: .... Date: ....

Circle the mistake in each sentence, and rewrite it correctly on the line.
(**Hint**: There is only one mistake in each sentence to correct.)

1. Ryan asked why we didn't invite he. ....

2. The foxs were chasing the rabbit. ....

3. The childs were excited about the circus. ....

4. Marys sister was born in this hospital. ....

5. Brittany love to climb trees. ....

6. Mary seen her favourite film last night. ....

7. The five goose were swimming in the pond. ....

8. Rebecca and i love ice-cream. ....

9. We picked the name kim for my hamster. ....

10. My doctor's name is Dr johnson. ....

My score: ____
10

My time: ....
minutes   seconds

Minute 87

Name: .... **Date:** ....

For Questions 1–5, circle the proper name for a person in each sentence.
(**Hint:** There is one proper name [noun] for a person in each sentence.)

1. Alana types fast on the computer.

2. Football is Martha's favourite sport.

3. Did you know that Justin is my cousin?

4. Tori washes her dog in the bathtub.

5. The librarian asked David to stop running.

For Questions 6–10, circle the noun (naming word) and underline the verb (action word) in each sentence.

6. Dinosaurs lived very long ago.

7. Our kites flew higher than ever.

8. The kids yelled all of a sudden.

9. My cat doesn't eat a lot anymore.

10. Why won't the young boy talk?

My score: —— / 10   **My time:** .... / ....
                                        minutes   seconds

Minute 88

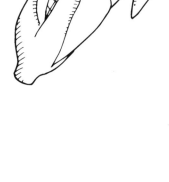

Name: .... **Date:** ....

Circle the describing words in each sentence.

(**Hint**: Each sentence has two describing words to circle.)

1. He wore a blue tie with the black suit.

2. The red house on the corner is big.

3. There are seven apples in the white bowl.

4. I grow yellow corn in my huge garden.

5. The loud noise scared the little girl.

6. I like sour and sweet flavours.

7. Cool water feels fresh during the summer.

8. The slimy snail slid across the hard ground.

9. Nicole's wool jumper was too hot to wear.

10. The soft blanket was made of pink fabric.

My score: ___
10

My time: ....
minutes   seconds

Minute 89

Name: .... **Date:** ....

For Questions 1–6, circle the nouns in each sentence that should begin with capital letters.
(**Hint**: Each sentence has two words that should begin with capital letters.)

1. amy went to hannah's house for dinner.

2. kira lives in the city of liverpool.

3. john works at grant Park on the weekends.

4. We will be on holiday in july and august.

5. i want to visit japan some day.

6. Next friday is the big christmas party.

For Questions 7–10, rewrite each sentence correctly on the line.
(**Hint**: There are two mistakes in each sentence to correct.)

7. Mrs kim comes on wednesdays.

....

8. We went to the bradman museum yesterday.

....

9. Our cats, mars and duke, are playful.

....

10. mr brady has six children.

....

My score: $\dfrac{\quad}{10}$ **My time:** ....
minutes   seconds

Minute 90

Name: .... **Date:** ....

Write the correct punctuation mark for the ending of each sentence.

1. My dad just won a brand-new car ....

2. Grace ate a hamburger for lunch ....

3. Do you want another glass of milk ....

4. I shopped for new shoes yesterday ....

5. What time is it ....

6. Don't you ever do that again ....

7. The cows are in the field ....

8. Amy is taking piano lessons ....

9. How are we going to get there ....

10. Heather is in bed reading a book ....

My score: $\dfrac{}{10}$

My time: ....
minutes   seconds

Minute 91

Name: .... **Date:** ....

For Questions 1–5, read each pair of sentences. Circle the correct sentence in each pair.

1. (a) Her is trying to win a contest.
   (b) She is trying to win a contest.

2. (a) We cant start the show without them.
   (b) We can't start the show without them.

3. (a) We are waiting for you.
   (b) Us are waiting for you.

4. (a) Larry and Jake is not happy.
   (b) Larry and Jake are not happy.

5. (a) I had an egg and cheese sandwich.
   (b) I had a egg and cheese sandwich.

For Questions 6–10, circle the mistake in each sentence and rewrite it correctly on the line.

6. Gary were late for school.   ....

7. The apple pie taste sweet.   ....

8. Ralph took John with he.   ....

9. Them are going to the dance.   ....

10. The clown has a read nose.   ....

My score: $\dfrac{}{10}$ **My time:** ....
                                                        minutes   seconds

Minute 92

Name: .... Date: ....

Read each group of words. Write C if each group of words is a complete sentence or I if it is incomplete.

1. Jack rescues the cat from the tree. ....

2. Myra cooks every night. ....

3. The elephants. ....

4. Kim spends all her money on pens. ....

5. Patsy puts lemon butter on her bread. ....

6. The hurt puppy. ....

7. Crawls on the floor. ....

8. Paula hopes it will not rain. ....

9. The balloons are too big. ....

10. The tiger in the tree. ....

My score: $\frac{\quad}{10}$

My time: ....
　　　　　　 minutes　　　　seconds

Name: .... **Date:** ....

**For Questions 1–5, circle whether each sentence is missing
a Noun or a Verb.**

1. The monkey .... two bananas.   Noun   Verb

2. Larry's new .... is lost.   Noun   Verb

3. Glenn .... the guitar and drums.   Noun   Verb

4. Brad .... three apples into the air.   Noun   Verb

5. Dorothy keeps her books on a ....   Noun   Verb

**For Questions 6–10, use a word from the box to complete each
sentence. Use each word only one time.**

| Susan | walked | I | make | orange |

6. The .... cat doesn't have a home.

7. Spiders .... webs to catch food.

8. .... waited for the school bus.

9. The choir .... across the stage.

10. Those gifts belong to my sister and ....

My score: $\dfrac{\quad}{10}$ **My time:** ....
                                                    minutes   seconds

Name: .... Date: ....

For Questions 1–5, read each set of words.
Circle the two homophones in each set.
(**Hint**: Remember that homophones are words that sound the same but are spelt differently and have different meanings.)

1. tail	tale	tall
2. raise	rose	rows
3. road	ride	rode
4. sale	safe	sail
5. pair	park	pear

For Questions 6–10, read each pair of sentences.
Circle the homophones in each pair.
(**Hint**: You must circle one word in each sentence.)

6. I am going to the market. I need two tomatoes.

7. Patty flew to Bali. She got the flu there.

8. I will pick clothes to wear. Then I will close my wardrobe.

9. He was sick all last week. He felt very weak and tired.

10. I would like to make a bird house. I need some wood.

My score: _____ / **10**

My time: ....
minutes   seconds

Minute 95

Name: .... **Date:** ....

Circle the mistake in each sentence and rewrite it correctly on the line.
(**Hint**: There is only one mistake in each sentence to correct.)

1. I had a apple with my lunch. ....

2. Him is sitting on the beach towel. ....

3. Mario and me are not going to the game. ....

4. The cat chasing the mouse last night. ....

5. Katie brush her teeth three times a day. ....

6. Kela has a new pair of glass. ....

7. Martin wear a jumper to school. ....

8. Chloe are not in school today. ....

9. Them are leaving the cinema early. ....

10. I is not ready for the test. ....

My score: $\dfrac{}{10}$ **My time:** ....
                                              minutes   seconds

Minute 96

Name: .... **Date:** ....

Write Yes *if each sentence is correct or* No *if it is not.*

1. I ate a hotdog, chips and cake for lunch. ....

2. The jackson family is going to Hong Kong. ....

3. jump high in the air Tommy can. ....

4. The fence needs to be painted. ....

5. The vase fell off the table. ....

6. Angela lives in Newcastle England. ....

7. The top of the hill was high. ....

8. Mary readed ten books in one weak. ....

9. We were glad when our noisy neighbours moved. ....

10. Kites are fun to flew. ....

My score: $\dfrac{}{10}$

My time: ....
minutes seconds

Minute 97

Name: .... Date: ....

For Questions 1–5, write Yes if each set of words is in alphabetical order or No if it is not.

1. water, hair, ice   ....

2. book, train, truck   ....

3. pea, flea, tea   ....

4. apple, banana, grapes   ....

5. crayon, eraser, pencil   ....

For Questions 6–10, put each set of words in alphabetical order.

6. milk, pan, egg   ....

7. snake, lion, pig   ....

8. red, blue, pink   ....

9. two, three, one   ....

10. write, colour, draw   ....

My score: ——
10

My time: ....
          minutes   seconds

Minute 98

Name: .... **Date:** ....

Circle the mistake in each sentence and rewrite it correctly on the line.

(**Hint:** There is only one mistake in each sentence to correct.)

1. Us went to my grandmother's house. ....

2. There are ate children on the team. ....

3. Please wash the dishs. ....

4. My mother is a pretty women. ....

5. The five child are playing with the dog. ....

6. These three branch must come down. ....

7. I no where the party is going to be. ....

8. Samantha house is next door. ....

9. Why is you going there? ....

10. I can swam five laps in my pool. ....

My score: $\dfrac{\quad}{10}$

My time: ....
           minutes   seconds

Minute 99

Name: .... Date: ....

Write the describing word that best completes each sentence.

1. An elephant is much .... than a tiger.
   big   bigger   biggest

2. My dad's truck is the .... one in the car show.
   nice   nicer   nicest

3. A bunny is .... than a snake.
   soft   softer   softest

4. Our big dog barks much .... than our small dog.
   loud   louder   loudest

5. That was the .... film I've ever seen.
   scary   scarier   scariest

6. That pig is the .... animal on the farm.
   fat   fatter   fattest

7. My hair is .... than my sister's hair.
   dark   darker   darkest

8. He is the .... kid I have ever met.
   mean   meaner   meanest

9. This jumper is .... than that one.
   warm   warmer   warmest

10. The lemonade tastes .... with sugar in it.
    sweet   sweeter   sweetest

My score: $\dfrac{}{10}$

My time: ....
minutes   seconds

Minute 100

Name: .... **Date:** ....

Write the correct present and past tense form in each sentence.

Present tense	Past tense

1. She .... her bike
         rides   rode
 every day.
	2. She .... her bike
	         rides rode
	 yesterday.

3. My dad .... us
       makes   made
 dinner sometimes.
	4. My dad ....
	       makes made
	 dinner all last week.

5. We usually ....
       eat   ate
 dinner early.
	6. Last night we ....
	       eat ate
	 dinner late.

7. The singer ....
       writes   wrote
 her own songs.
	8. She even ....
	       writes wrote
	 a song for her mother.

9. Maria never ....
       loses   lost
 anything.
	10. Maria has never
	 .... anything
	       loses lost
	 before.

My score: $\dfrac{}{10}$ **My time:** ....

                                           minutes   seconds

www.prim-ed.com   Prim-Ed Publishing®

Minute answer key

Minute 1
1. cap
2. gap
3. lap
4. map
5. nap
6. rap
7. sap
8. tap
9. yap
10. zap

Minute 2
1. gap
2. get
3. go
4. can
5. cot
6. cut
7. bat
8. bed
9. bit
10. bug

Minute 3
1. Yes
2. No
3. No
4. Yes
5. Yes
6. No
7. Yes
8. No
9. No
10. Yes

Minute 4
1. My
2. I
3. The
4. Susan
5. He
6. Birds
7. How
8. She
9. Sweets
10. Danny

Minute 5
1. .
2. ?
3. .
4. !
5. ?
6. .
7. !
8. .
9. ?
10. ?

Minute 6
1. Complete
2. Not complete
3. Complete
4. Not complete
5. Complete
6. Complete
7. Not complete
8. Complete
9. Complete
10. Not complete

Minute 7
1. a
2. b
3. b
4. b
5. a
6. b
7. b
8. a
9. b
10. a

Minute 8
1. T
2. A
3. A
4. E
5. T
6. E
7. T
8. A
9. E
10. T

Minute 9
1. The circus
2. Lucy and Cindy
3. My mother
4. John
5. The boy
6. Spiders
7. The clouds
8. Mackenzie and Kaylin
9. I
10. The birds

Minute 10
1. works in the garden.
2. rakes the leaves.
3. watches us play.
4. jump into the leaves.
5. chases me.
6. picks up rubbish.
7. mows the lawn.
8. makes lunch.
9. eat when we are done.
10. looks nice.

Minute 11
1. ant
2. bird
3. bug
4. cat
5. dog
6. duck
7. fish
8. fox
9. ox
10. pig

Minute 12
1. a
2. b
3. a
4. a
5. b
6. !
7. .
8. ?
9. .
10. ?

Minute 13
1. Not complete
2. Complete
3. Complete
4. Not complete
5. My kitten is white.
6. I like to read stories.
7. Our teacher is funny.
8. A
9. E
10. T

Minute 14
1. Chris
2. The candle
3. The bat
4. My parents
5. Mr Barton
6. chases the cat.
7. hops away.
8. sits on the flower.
9. tells funny stories.
10. jumps up.

Minute 15
1. Nia
2. baby
3. teacher
4. Ryan
5. woman
6. father
7. Sarah
8. postman
9. zookeeper
10. Shawn

Minute 16
1. school
2. classroom
3. library
4. cafe
5. bathroom
6. outside
7. playground
8. office
9. park
10. store

Minute 17
1. crayons
2. story
3. coat
4. milk
5. scissors
6. clock
7. homework
8. money
9. dress
10. paper

Minute 18
1. birds
2. cat
3. fish
4. dog
5. monkeys
6. cow
7. shark
8. lion
9. puppy
10. camel

Minute 19
1. Ms Watson
2. Debra Hill
3. Dr Young
4. Uncle Max
5. Officer Jones
6. Mike Chan
7. Miss Jenkins
8. Mrs Patrick
9. Aunt Meg
10. Grandfather Joe

Minute 20
1. Stone Park
2. Stirling Street
3. Dubbo Primary
4. Simple Salad
5. Jeans Now
6. Manchester
7. United Kingdom
8. Dublin Airport
9. Ocean World
10. Chinatown

Minute answer key

Minute 21
1. Ming
2. Oscar
3. Roxy
4. Shimmer
5. Venom
6. Duke
7. Fluffy
8. Muffin
9. Simon
10. Nella

Minute 22
1. Saturday
2. June
3. Easter
4. New Year's
5. September
6. Friday
7. Valentine's
8. October
9. Tuesday
10. April

Minute 23
1. Our dog ran on Monday, Wednesday and Saturday.
2. Would you like chocolate, strawberry or vanilla ice-cream?
3. Samantha likes apples, grapes and bananas.
4. Tennis, netball and squash are her favourite sports.
5. Does Bruce prefer lettuce, carrots or potatoes?
6. No
7. No
8. Yes
9. Yes
10. No

Minute 24
1. Paris, France
2. Madrid, Spain
3. Dublin, Ireland
4. London, England
5. Lima, Peru
6. Bogota, Colombia
7. Tokyo, Japan
8. Cairo, Egypt
9. Wellington, New Zealand
10. Buenos Aires, Argentina

Minute 25
1. Apples, bananas
2. girl, sisters
3. pupils, playground
4. friend, bike
5. class, library
6. desks, chairs
7. cat, rug
8. flowers, garden
9. torch, room
10. food, party

Minute 26
1. Thing
2. Place
3. Person
4. Place
5. Animal
6. Person
7. Thing
8. Animal
9. Person
10. Animal

Minute 27
1. France
2. John
3. February
4. Saturday
5. Easter
6. Maria
7. Carter
8. Choco
9. Monday
10. Melville

Minute 28
1. Can Emma, Liz and Ben come to the park?
2. We need pens, pencils and paper.
3. Would you like cake, ice-cream or a doughnut?
4. Chicago, Miami and New York are my favourite cities.
5. Invite Geraldine, Diane and Jennifer.
6. Vancouver, Canada
7. Sydney, Australia
8. Nairobi, Kenya
9. Mexico City, Mexico
10. Pretoria, South Africa

Minute 29
1. sings
2. reads
3. play
4. say
5. grows
6. give
7. swim
8. rises
9. skips
10. picks

Minute 30
1. clap
2. love
3. fall
4. help
5. jumps
6. fly
7. eat
8. blows
9. make
10. run

Minute 31
1. pets
2. chops
3. bakes
4. paints
5. chases
6. plays
7. makes
8. runs
9. licks
10. barks

Minute 32
1. played
2. smelled
3. pulled
4. watched
5. jumped
6. cooked
7. asked
8. looked
9. named
10. painted

Minute 33
1. am
2. Are
3. is
4. are
5. are
6. am
7. is
8. are
9. are
10. is

Minute 34
1. was
2. were
3. was
4. was
5. were
6. was
7. were
8. was
9. were
10. was

Minute 35
1. No
2. Yes
3. Yes
4. Yes
5. No
6. No
7. No
8. Yes
9. Yes
10. Yes

Minute 36
1. cars
2. songs
3. beds
4. pets
5. aeroplanes
6. streets
7. bugs
8. books
9. games
10. trees

Minute 37
1. foxes
2. dishes
3. couches
4. bushes
5. glasses
6. buses
7. watches
8. boxes
9. beaches
10. classes

Minute 38
1. hills
2. peaches
3. circuses
4. spoons
5. wishes
6. hands
7. foxes
8. coins
9. branches
10. birds

Minute 39
1. eat
2. pet
3. paints
4. ran
5. grew
6. went
7. melted
8. go
9. walked
10. takes

Minute 40
1. Past
2. Present
3. Present
4. Past
5. Present
6. Present
7. Past
8. Past
9. Present
10. Past

Prim-Ed Publishing®
www.prim-ed.com

Minute answer key

Minute 41
1. had
2. were
3. is
4. am
5. are
6. is
7. had
8. have
9. was
10. has

Minute 42
1. cows
2. cups
3. witches
4. pails
5. foxes
6. hats
7. girls
8. dishes
9. shops
10. wishes

Minute 43
1. I
2. me
3. me
4. I
5. me
6. I
7. me
8. I
9. I
10. me

Minute 44
1. her
2. her
3. She
4. she
5. her
6. She
7. her
8. She
9. her
10. her

Minute 45
1. He
2. He
3. him
4. him
5. He
6. He
7. him
8. He
9. He
10. him

Minute 46
1. They
2. They
3. them
4. They
5. them
6. them
7. They
8. They
9. them
10. They

Minute 47
1. We
2. us
3. us
4. We
5. us
6. No
7. Yes
8. No
9. No
10. Yes

Minute 48
1. little
2. tall
3. big
4. long
5. small
6. round
7. square
8. flat
9. oval
10. skinny

Minute 49
1. pink
2. two
3. blue
4. four
5. three
6. red
7. black
8. yellow
9. five
10. three

Minute 50
1. sweet
2. sour
3. spicy
4. clean
5. minty
6. yummy
7. tasty
8. rotten
9. creamy
10. stinky

Minute 51
1. soft
2. loud
3. fuzzy
4. hard
5. squeaky
6. silky
7. squealing
8. chirping
9. rough
10. sharp

Minute 52
1. taller
2. easier
3. bigger
4. hotter
5. older
6. longer
7. colder
8. faster
9. nicer
10. higher

Minute 53
1. strongest
2. smallest
3. oldest
4. funniest
5. longest
6. No
7. Yes
8. No
9. Yes
10. Yes

Minute 54
1. No
2. Yes
3. No
4. Yes
5. No
6. Yes
7. No
8. Yes
9. No
10. No

Minute 55
1. She
2. them
3. him
4. us
5. her
6. He
7. They
8. me
9. her
10. her

Minute 56
1. tall, spicy
2. dark, big
3. red, white
4. sweet, tall
5. warm, furry
6. black, rotten
7. one, two
8. square, soft
9. dark, chocolate
10. loud, quiet

Minute 57
1. longer
2. tallest
3. later
4. cutest
5. cleanest
6. taller
7. smallest
8. sweeter
9. nicer
10. loudest

Minute 58
1. Sally's
2. plane's
3. cat's
4. Dean's
5. Maria's
6. tree's
7. park's
8. computer's
9. bunny's
10. Becky's

Minute 59
1. Yes
2. No
3. Yes
4. Yes
5. No
6. c
7. d
8. a
9. e
10. b

Minute 60
1. makes
2. sings
3. talks
4. wag
5. washes
6. fly
7. loses
8. rides
9. run
10. drives

Minute answer key

Minute 61
1. hug
2. runs
3. plays
4. buy
5. bake
6. throws
7. blows
8. skips
9. read
10. make

Minute 62
1. children
2. elves
3. mice
4. geese
5. teeth
6. women
7. men
8. feet
9. people
10. leaves

Minute 63
1. children
2. shelves
3. teeth
4. lives
5. feet
6. men
7. wolves
8. women
9. geese
10. mice

Minute 64
1. saw
2. left
3. fed
4. lost
5. drank
6. wrote
7. ate
8. fell
9. swam
10. drove

Minute 65
1. made
2. wrote
3. fell
4. broke
5. took
6. saw
7. ran
8. ate
9. came
10. said

Minute 66
1. an
2. a
3. a
4. an
5. an
6. a
7. a
8. an
9. an
10. a

Minute 67
1. The
2. An or The
3. an or the
4. A or The
5. A or The
6. the
7. a
8. an or the
9. an
10. The

Minute 68
1. Maggie's
2. Carrie's
3. girl's
4. Bob's
5. dog's
6. No
7. Yes
8. Yes
9. No
10. Yes

Minute 69
1. swims
2. watched
3. like
4. dive
5. raced
6. wins
7. takes
8. washed
9. rings
10. does

Minute 70
1. More than one
2. One
3. One
4. More than one
5. More than one
6. Present
7. Past
8. Past
9. Present
10. Past

Minute 71
1. No
2. Yes
3. Yes
4. Yes
5. Yes
6. No
7. Yes
8. No
9. Yes
10. Yes

Minute 72
1. bedroom
2. backyard
3. shoelaces
4. sunshine
5. jellyfish
6. homemade
7. homework
8. grandchildren
9. breakfast
10. walkway

Minute 73
1. Yes
2. No
3. No
4. Yes
5. Yes
6. No
7. Yes
8. Yes
9. No
10. Yes

Minute 74
1. isn't
2. hasn't
3. don't
4. can't
5. won't
6. haven't
7. don't
8. shouldn't
9. won't
10. isn't

Minute 75
1. d
2. e
3. a
4. f
5. b
6. c
7. we're
8. you're
9. she's
10. I'm

Minute 76
1. happy
2. large
3. pretty
4. quick
5. shout
6. c
7. e
8. d
9. b
10. a

Minute 77
1. hot, warm
2. see, look
3. fat, thick
4. sleep, nap
5. kind, nice
6. close, shut
7. big
8. jumps
9. sad
10. likes

Minute 78
1. Yes
2. No
3. Yes
4. No
5. Yes
6. young, old
7. push, pull
8. hard, soft
9. clean, dirty
10. right, left

Minute 79
1. off
2. thin
3. dry
4. open
5. night
6. end
7. c
8. d
9. b
10. a

Minute 80
1. Yes
2. No
3. Yes
4. Yes
5. No
6. Yes
7. d
8. c
9. a
10. b

Minute answer key

Minute 81
1. wear, where
2. know, no
3. our, hour
4. hear, here
5. sea, see
6. so, sew
7. knew, new
8. four, for
9. deer, dear
10. meet, meat

Minute 82
1. starfish
2. bedroom
3. doorbell
4. doghouse
5. blackbird
6. snowball
7. sailboat
8. sunshine
9. shoelace
10. sandpit

Minute 83
1. she is
2. we are
3. should not
4. do not
5. I am
6. he's
7. Don't
8. can't
9. hasn't
10. we're

Minute 84
1. A
2. S
3. A
4. A
5. S
6. A
7. A
8. S
9. A
10. S

Minute 85
1. flew
2. meet
3. sea
4. hour
5. won
6. whole
7. eye
8. son
9. tail
10. Would

Minute 86
1. he/him
2. foxs/foxes
3. childs/children
4. Marys/Mary's
5. love/loves
6. seen/saw
7. goose/geese
8. i/I
9. kim/Kim
10. johnson/Johnson

Minute 87
1. Alana
2. Martha's
3. Justin
4. Tori
5. David
6. noun: dinosaurs; verb: lived
7. noun: kites; verb: flew
8. noun: kids; verb: yelled
9. noun: cat; verb: eat
10. noun: boy; verb: talk

Minute 88
1. blue, black
2. red, big
3. seven, white
4. yellow, huge
5. loud, little
6. sour, sweet
7. cool, fresh
8. slimy, hard
9. wool, hot
10. soft, pink

Minute 89
1. amy, hannah's
2. kira, liverpool
3. john, grant
4. july, august
5. i, japan
6. friday, christmas
7. Mrs Kim comes on Wednesdays.
8. We went to Bradman Museum yesterday.
9. Our cats Mars and Duke are playful.
10. Mr Brady has six children.

Minute 90
1. !
2. .
3. ?
4. .
5. ?
6. !
7. .
8. .
9. ?
10. .

Minute 91
1. b
2. b
3. a
4. b
5. a
6. were/was
7. taste/tasted or tastes
8. he/him
9. Them/They
10. read/red

Minute 92
1. C
2. C
3. I
4. C
5. C
6. I
7. I
8. C
9. C
10. I

Minute 93
1. Verb
2. Noun
3. Verb
4. Verb
5. Noun
6. orange
7. make
8. Susan
9. walked
10. I

Minute 94
1. tail, tale
2. rose, rows
3. road, rode
4. sale, sail
5. pair, pear
6. to, two
7. flew, flu
8. clothes, close
9. week, weak
10. would, wood

Minute 95
1. a/an
2. Him/He
3. me/I
4. chasing/chased
5. brush/brushes
6. glass/glasses
7. wear/wears or wore
8. are/is
9. Them/They
10. is/am

Minute 96
1. Yes
2. No
3. No
4. Yes
5. Yes
6. No
7. Yes
8. No
9. Yes
10. No

Minute 97
1. No
2. Yes
3. No
4. Yes
5. Yes
6. egg, milk, pan
7. lion, pig, snake
8. blue, pink, red
9. one, three, two
10. colour, draw, write

Minute 98
1. Us/We
2. ate/eight
3. dishs/dishes
4. women/woman
5. child/children
6. branch/branches
7. no/know
8. Samantha/ Samantha's
9. is/are
10. swam/swim

Minute 99
1. bigger
2. nicest
3. softer
4. louder
5. scariest
6. fattest
7. darker
8. meanest
9. warmer
10. sweeter

Minute 100
1. rides
2. rode
3. makes
4. made
5. eat
6. ate
7. writes
8. wrote
9. loses
10. lost